D1599564

Thank you for purchasing your copy of Joyfully Josie!

You are now a part of a very meaningful mission! Every book purchased helps towards a cure for FOXG1 syndrome and many more childhood neurological diseases.

To join Josie's playground and learn more visit www.JoyfullyJosie.love

Live Joyfully,

Josie

Joyfully Josie

Written by **Nicole Zeitzer Johnson**

Illustrations by **David Concepcion**

www.joyfullyJosie.love
www.foxg1research.org

Printed in USA
Published by the FOXG1 RESEARCH FOUNDATION
IBSN print: 979-8-218-15977-1
IBSN ebook: 979-8-9882329-0-2
10 9 8 7 6 5 4 3 2 1
First hardcover edition May, 2023
Illustrations by David Concepcion
Edited by Brooke Vitale
Layout by Lindsay Broderick

FOXG1®
RESEARCH
FOUNDATION
WWW.FOXG1RESEARCH.ORG

For Josie and her FOXG1 friends who choose joy and spread love, even through the most challenging times.

—NZJ

Meet Josie.

Josie is just like other
girls her age.

She loves music, sunny days,
and playing with friends.

But, Josie is different from other kids in one big way: she was born with a rare disease called FOXG1 syndrome.

FOXG1 syndrome causes many problems for children who are born with it.

FOXG1 syndrome causes Josie to have disabilities.

Abilities are things someone is "able" to do.

Disabilities are things someone is "not able" to do.

Josie is *not able* to talk.

Josie is *not able* to walk.

Josie is *not able* to sit up without falling over.

She is disabled.

One sunny day, Josie's mom takes Josie to the playground.

Josie sees the other
children playing
and laughing.

The sound of their laughter makes Josie so happy. The more they laugh, the more Josie laughs, too!

A little boy looks over when he hears Josie's laughter. He wants to join the fun, too.

When he sees Josie's wheelchair, he gets a little nervous. But, Josie flashes her big, adorable smile as if she is saying, "It's okay, come say hi to me."

"Hi, I'm Steven. What's your name?"

Josie's mommy gives Josie a tray
with a big blue button on it.

Giggling, Josie hits the button,
which says...

"Josie!"

"Josie? Your name is Josie! I'm so happy to meet you," says Steven. "Josie, would you like to be friends?"

Josie's mom puts two new buttons on Josie's tray, then steps back so Josie can answer.

Josie tries to hit the yes button,
but she misses.

Josie's mom explains to Steven, "Josie has a rare disease called FOXG1 syndrome. It causes her to have some disabilities.

For example, she is not always able to move her body the way she wants to."

Steven smiles at his new friend.
"That's okay Josie, keep trying."

Josie tries again.

This time she hits the green button!

"Good job, Josie!" Steven cheers.

Instead of hitting a button, Josie uses her voice to say,

"Yeah!"

"She just learned to say 'yeah!'"
Josie's mom says, beaming with joy.

Suddenly, the music from an ice cream truck fills the air.

"Yum! Ice cream!" Steven says. "Josie, would you like an ice cream cone?"

This time, Josie doesn't hit a button.

Josie's mommy shakes her head and says, "Josie isn't able to eat food like we do.

FOXG1 syndrome makes it too difficult to swallow safely. Josie is fed through this tube attached to her belly. Don't worry, it doesn't hurt!"

Steven says, "You're so happy Josie. Even with all your disabilities, you love to see the joy all around."

From now on, I'm going to call you
'Joyfully Josie!' Is that ok?"

Josie looks Steven right in the eye and with just one try she hits the green button.

"YES!"

Fact Page

FOXG1 syndrome is one of many rare diseases that cause children to have different kinds of disabilities.

If you see a child that looks different from other children, don't forget these FIVE Things that Josie taught us.

1. Children with disabilities love to be included; they just have to play in different ways.

2. Don't be afraid to ask questions so that you can get to know each other.

3. There are ways to communicate with someone who isn't able to talk—like with buttons.

4. If you're patient, you may make a new friend!

5. No matter how hard things are, you can always choose to be joyful—like Josie!

About the Author:

Nicole Zeitzer Johnson is on a mission to find a cure for the rare disease her daughter Josie was born with, called FOXG1 syndrome. She co-founded the **FOXG1 Research Foundation,** which is dedicated to improving the lives of every child in the world with FOXG1 syndrome and related disorders. Nicole created

the Joyfully Josie series of children's books and a digital platform to help all children understand disabilities. Before becoming a champion for rare diseases, Nicole worked as a television producer and was also an entrepreneur in the music business. Nicole lives in New York with her husband, Richard, and Josie's big brother, Tanner.

About FOXG1 syndrome:

FOXG1 syndrome is a rare disease that happens when an important gene called foxg1 doesn't work properly. Children born with FOXG1 syndrome often have a hard time talking, walking, doing things on their own, and they often have terrible seizures. But, there are people who are working very hard to change this. The FOXG1 Research Foundation is a group of scientists, doctors, and families who are working together to find a cure and bring hope and healing to children around the world. FOXG1 children all have one thing in common—they are amazing. Despite their many challenges, just like Josie, they show us how to appreciate the little things in life and teach us about strength, love, and pure joy.

Meet Josie and watch her sweet laughter at www.JoyfullyJosie.love

Learn all about FOXG1 syndrome at www.foxg1research.org

Look out for **more books from Joyfully Josie** that answer many questions children have about disabilities and rare diseases!

CPSIA information can be obtained
at www.ICGtesting.com
Printed in the USA
BVHW010726220523
664542BV00001B/1